Lisa Bastien &

INTERVALS
THROUGH A FIFTH

THEORY BOOSTERS SERIES

ISBN-10: 0-8497-7381-4
ISBN-13: 978-0-8497-7381-5

HOW NOTES MOVE ON THE STAFF

Here are three ways that notes can move on the staff:

Repeat — same note
Step — consecutive notes
Skips — skips a line / skips a space

Identify the way these notes move on the staff.

1. Repeat

2. _____

3. _____

4. _____

5. _____

6. _____

MATCHING

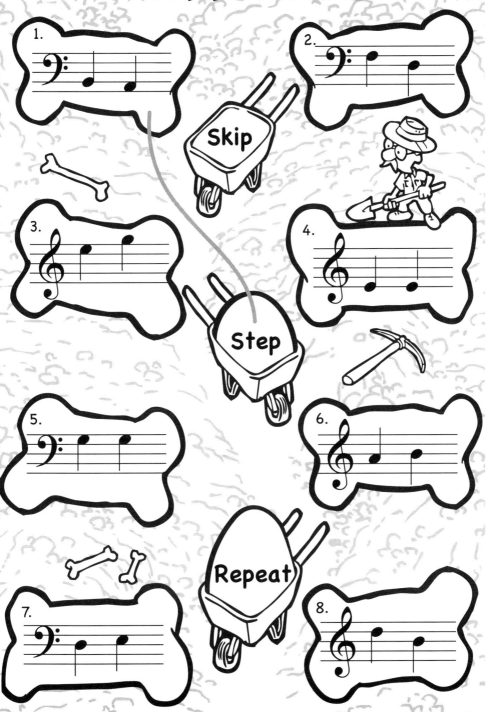

MEASURING INTERVALS

The distance between two notes is called an **interval.**

On the keys, a 2nd is like a step from one key to the next:

2ND F G A B
2nd   2nd

Write an interval of a 2nd up or down from the given letters.

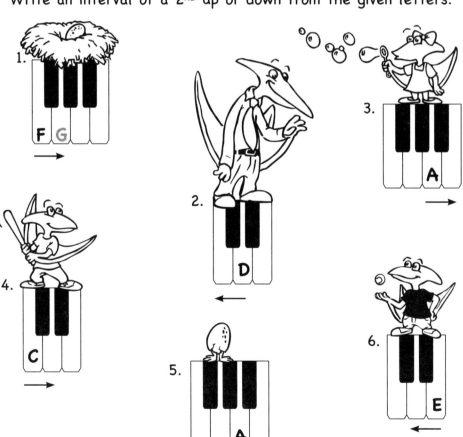

1. F G →

2. D ←

3. A →

4. C →

5. A ←

6. E ←

On the staff, a 2nd is like a step:

Up a 2nd   Down a 2nd

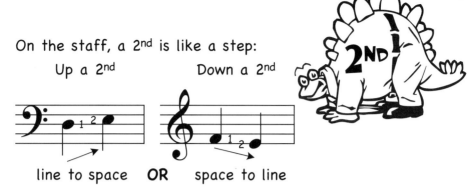

line to space   **OR**   space to line

Draw the note that is an interval of a 2nd up or down from the one given.

On the keys, a 3rd is like a skip:

G ● B
3rd

Skip a key.

Write the letter name that is an interval of a 3rd up or down from the one given.

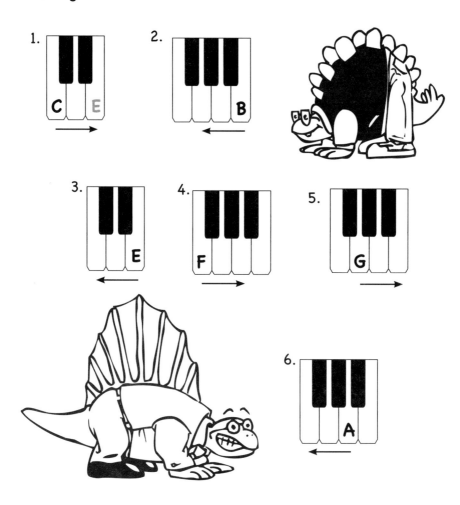

1. C   E →

2. B ←

3. E ←

4. F →

5. G →

6. A ←

On the staff, a 3rd is like a skip:

Draw the note that is an interval of a 3rd up or down from the one given.

MATCHING

CROSSWORD FUN

ACROSS

2. The interval that is like a step.

4. Another word for a 2nd.

5.

DOWN

1. The interval that is like a skip.

2. Another word for a 3rd.

3. The term that means "the distance between two notes."

KP26

On the keys, a 4th is a larger skip:

4th

Skip two keys.

Write the letter name that is an interval of a 4th up or down from the one given.

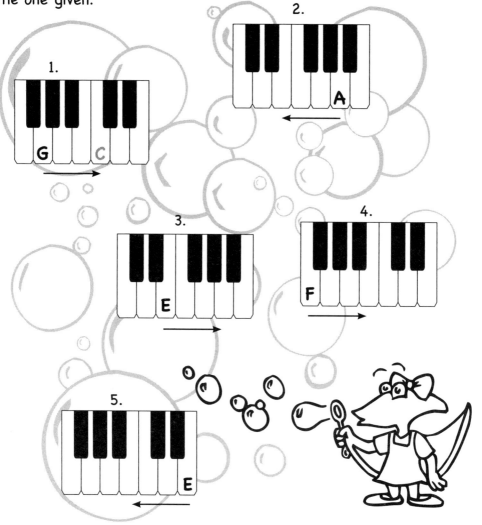

KP26

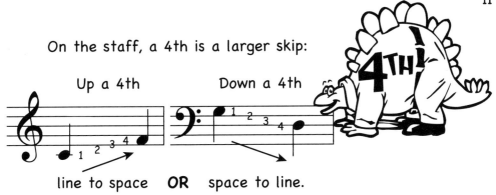

On the staff, a 4th is a larger skip:

Up a 4th   Down a 4th

line to space   **OR**   space to line.

Draw the note that is an interval of a 4th up or down from the one given.

KP26

On the keys, a 5th is a larger skip:

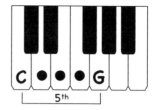

C ● ● ● G

5th

Skip three keys.

Write the letter name that is an interval of a 5th up or down from the one given.

1. C   G

2. D

3. E

4. A

5. C

On the staff, a 5th is a larger skip:

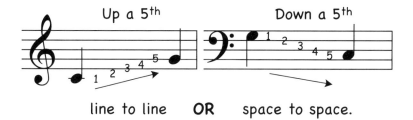

Up a 5th   Down a 5th

line to line   **OR**   space to space.

Draw the note that is an interval of a 5th up or down from the one given.

1.

2.

3.

4.

5.

6.

14

Color the 4ths blue and the 5ths red.

SEARCH FOR A MATCH

☑ Second   ☐ Interval   ☐ Step   ☐ Fourth

☐ Third   ☐ Skip   ☐ Repeat   ☐ Fifth

P	Q	B	A	L	I	R	O	N	Z
F	I	F	T	H	S	B	G	F	E
D	N	B	Q	R	E	K	L	M	T
C	T	C	D	O	C	E	I	H	F
A	E	G	I	H	O	J	I	P	H
O	R	K	P	L	N	R	S	V	T
M	V	W	E	X	D	E	Y	Z	R
R	A	H	B	D	G	P	H	J	U
P	L	E	H	I	O	E	U	M	O
F	S	T	E	P	S	A	H	I	F
K	L	N	S	R	E	T	V	W	E

KP26

MELODIC INTERVALS

Melodic intervals are single notes played one at a time, like notes in a melody.

2nd   3rd   4th   5th

A. Write the name of each melodic interval.
B. Play these notes on the piano.

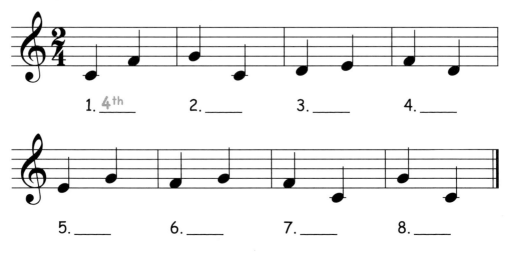

1. 4th   2. ____   3. ____   4. ____

5. ____   6. ____   7. ____   8. ____

HARMONIC INTERVALS

Harmonic intervals are two notes played together to make harmony in music.

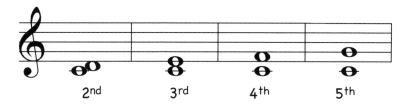

2nd   3rd   4th   5th

A. Write the name of each harmonic interval.
B. Play these notes on the piano.

1. _5th_   2. ____   3. ____   4. ____

5. ____   6. ____   7. ____   8. ____

MATCHING

1.

2.

3.

4.

5.

6.

7.

8.

9.

10.

WRITING INTERVALS

A. Draw one quarter note to complete each melodic interval.

B. Play these notes on the piano.

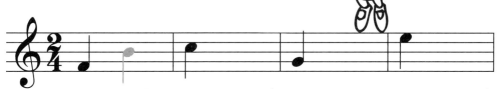

1. Up a 4th   2. Down a 2nd   3. Up a 5th   4. Down a 3rd

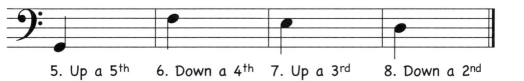

5. Up a 5th   6. Down a 4th   7. Up a 3rd   8. Down a 2nd

What did the bull say when he ran out of cash?

"I guess I'll just charge it!"

KP26

A. Name each interval.
B. Play these notes on the piano.

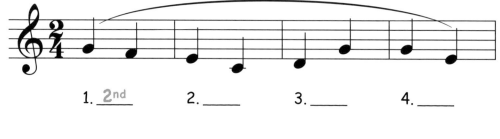

1. _2nd_   2. ____   3. ____   4. ____

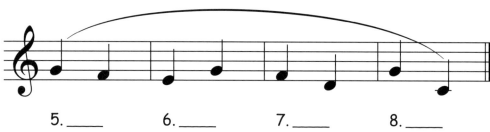

5. ____   6. ____   7. ____   8. ____

Why didn't the cow want to make his bed?

Because he wasn't in
the moooood!

A. Name each interval.
B. Play these notes on the piano.

1. <u>5th</u> 2. _____ 3. _____ 4. _____

5. _____ 6. _____ 7. _____ 8. _____

How does a pig treat a rash?

He uses oinkment!

Color the: 2nds green   4ths red
             3rds blue   5ths purple